DUNG BEETLE WELL-LOVED TALE

KEY SUBTEXTS is a scheme exclusive to
Dung Beetle Books, where children are given
stepping stones to the interior meaning of a
surface text. These come in the form of three
key words, each of which give a clue to the
author's deeply sinister intent.

Eventually your children will learn to confuse
insight with paranoia, and so develop a healthy,
progressive outlook.

This book belongs to:

DUNG BEETLE

'WELL-LOVED TALES.'

Marina & the Curse of the Royal Yugoslavian Academy of Art

Retold inaccurately by M Elia
Illustrated by M Elia

Once upon a time, in the land of Yugoslavia, in the heart of the woods there lived a hard-working mother of many, many, many children called Marina.

She lived in a humble cottage with no electricity or running water, and a massive brutalist extension at the back.

new words   brutalised   cottage   extension

Every morning Marina would wake at dawn
to chop firewood, scrub nappies and engage
in life threatening performance art.

It was a tough life, but she did not complain.

Marina ran the house with military precision.
At 8am she would descend from the ceiling
naked, with a snake around her neck.

"Good morning children - I love you, but you
are a *disaster* for my work."

The children nodded in agreement.
Every breakfast was a lesson.

new words
happy   disaster   family

The first class of the day was cookery.

Marina left the children with boiling water, sharp knives and flaming pizza ovens.

When she returned, she was always disappointed by their mediocre ideas.

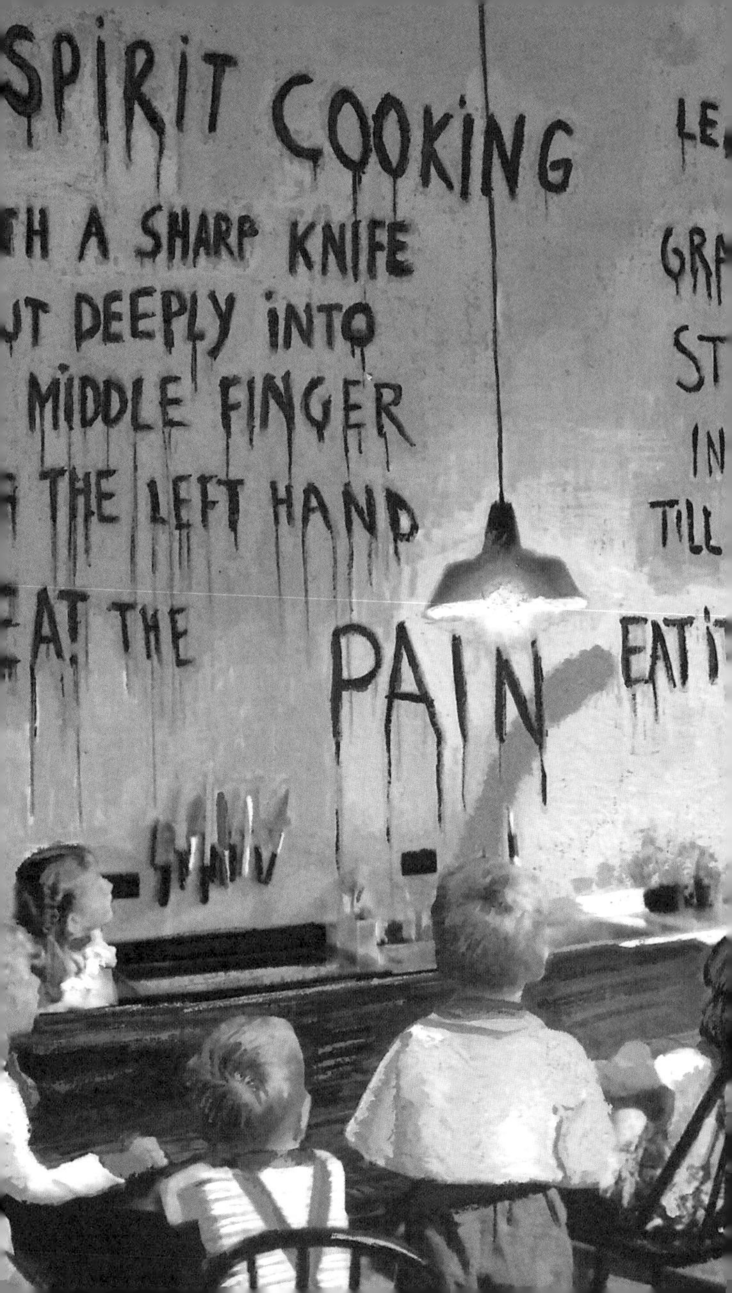

SPIRIT COOKING
A SHARP KNIFE
DEEPLY INTO
MIDDLE FINGER
THE LEFT HAND
AT THE
PAIN
TILL

The children do better in their morning prayers.

"Today, and every day, we ask you to please accept mummy to the Royal Academy of Yugoslavian Art. May her solo retrospective come true. Amen."

"No woman has ever been shown in The Royal Academy of Yugoslavia! "
Marina reminded her children.

"Certainly not a performance artist!" said the children.

new words
pray   for   mummy

After forest school, the children relaxed in the garden, whilst Marina filmed herself being violently assaulted by members of the public.

The Royal Academy of Yugoslavia
existed in the shadow of a 500 year curse,
cast by a wicked witch with no artistic talent.

new words

real   reason   witchcraft

The legend told that the witch turned any woman artist attempting to enter the Royal Academy of Yugoslavia into a duck!

Doomed to quack forever and ever, whilst shitting on the art that had sunk to the bottom of the Academy's pond.

.

new words

woman   art   doomed

Every full moon, while Marina levitated, the wicked witch came to cackle at her.

 "Your 'performance' will never be accepted! The people of Yugoslavia care not for your ex-boyfriend!"

Marina always fell back to the ground.

new words

get   over   it

However much the witch tried to undermine her, Marina never lost sight of her dream.

As she gazed wistfully out of the kitchen window, she saw herself scrubbing the blood from a human skeleton, forever and ever and ever.

new words

domestic   bliss   escape

One morning, while her children longed
for breakfast, Marina decided enough
was enough. She would go to the
Royal Academy of Yugoslavia and
defeat the witch.

"I won't spend the rest of my life
as a domestic slave!" she informed
her children.

new words

slave   defeat   breakfast

Marina gathered her babies together.

"You will live with your
grandmother in Belgrade.
I will defeat the witch.

Then we will see."

new words

turn   life   around

The children pretend to be sad.

"Goodbye, mother! We look forward to your solo show at the Royal Academy of Yugoslavia!"

They are escorted through the woods by a giant owl, a small donkey and the social services.

new words
      state   swallows   children

Marina packed a sack with bread, olive oil
and a pocket knife for sporadic
performances, and walked all the way
to The Royal Academy of Yugoslavia,
determined to defeat the witch.

But the witch was gazing at Marina in her looking glass.

"Curse you, attention seeker!" rambled the witch. "You will now understand real pain! Art fans of Yugoslavia will feed you crumbs as you drift on a stagnant pond until death."

new words

stagnant   death   quack

The witch appeared in Marina's path.

"You will never make
celebrity friends! "

She began speaking in tongues, and
they all said the same thing.

"You will never have a
performance art show!"

new words

celebrity   tongue   performance

But Marina was secretly filming.

Her art trapped the witch in a sub-par video installation on loop. Everyone's worst nightmare.

The curse was instantly reversed.

witch   on   loop

Days later, news of Marina's victory spread around the kingdom. The people of Yugoslavia cheered and self-harmed in celebration.

new words

        sack   head   festival

Marina had made it, and her work was accepted into the Academy.

Her fame enabled her to liberate the ducks, so that they rightfully shared a table with Yugoslavia's most illustrious art critics.

new words

defecate   on   academy

New words used in this book

6 brutalised / cottage / extension

8 scrub / soiled / performance

10 happy / disaster / family

12 middle / finger / pizza

14 pray / for / mummy

16 happy / child / play

18 real / reason / witchcraft

20 woman / art/ doomed

22 get / over / it

24 domestic / bliss / escape

26 slave / defeat / breakfast

28 turn / life / around

30 state / swallows / children

32 sporadic / knife/ sandwich

34 stagnant / death / quack

36 celebrity /tongue / performance

38 witch / on / loop

40 sack / head / festival

42 defecate / on / academy

Total number of new words 57

First published by Dung Beetle ltd 2023 © Miriam Elia

Photography by Becky Philp   Edited by Tania Edwards   Modelled by Sarah Bagner
With special thanks to Marina Abramović , Todd Eckert and Ruth Sallon Elia

The History of Dung Beetle books

Dung Beetle are an educational publishing house founded in 1936 in Dunging, a small English village renowned for the high quality of its manure. Originally set up by a family of retired Presbyterian manure workers, the founders set out to deliver to children's publishing the same fine standards of workmanship and attention to detail they once did to dung.

More recent titles include:

We go to the gallery   2014
We learn at home   2016
We go out   2016
We do Christmas   2018
We do Lockdown   2020
We see the sights   2022
Things to make & do   2023

Dung Beetle continue to produce high quality books and early learning tools which cover a range of sensitive or difficult topics. Their key goal is simple: to embed core literacy and numeracy skills into children's first knowledge of evil and death.

*Est doctrina de stercore**

*From shit comes learning

For just as the humble Dung Beetle gathers faeces from the forest floor in which to lay its eggs, the child lays 'eggs of knowledge' in the turd of its own mind.

Notes / Things I found offensive